Meet the friends

Illustrated by Nina O'Connell

Nelson

Down the hill

Ben the dog
went down the hill.
"Look at me.
Look at me," said Ben.

Jip the cat

went down the hill.

"Look at me.

Look at me," said Jip.

Sam the fox

went down the hill.

"Look at me.

Look at me," said Sam.

"Look at me," said Ben.

"Look at me," said Jip.

"Look at me," said Sam.

Sam wants to play

Sam the fox

went to see Ben.

"Will you play with me?"

"No, I won't," said Ben.

Sam the fox

went to see Meg.

"Will you play with me?"

"No, I won't," said Meg.

Sam the fox

went to see Jip.

"Will you play with me?"

"No, I won't," said Jip.

Sam the fox
went to see Deb.
"Will you play with me?"
"Yes, I will," said Deb.

Help me

Jip the cat ran up the tree.
"Help, help," said Jip.

"Can I help you?" said Pat the pig.

"No, you can't," said Jip.

"Can I help you?" said Ben.

"No, you can't," said Jip.

"Can I help you?" said Sam.

"No, you can't," said Jip.

"Can I help you?" said Deb.

"Yes, you can," said Jip.

A game

Can you crawl down
the caterpillar?
Read the words to
reach his tail.

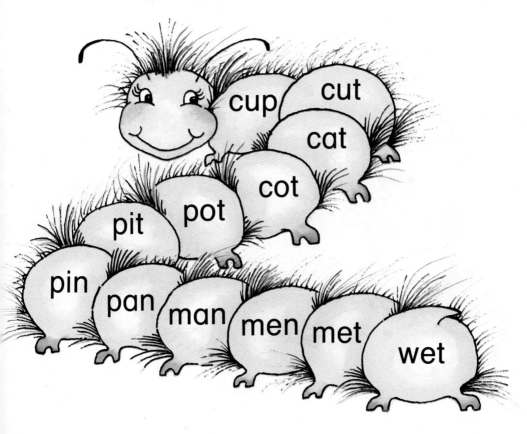